CORNELIUS GURLITT
(1820 - 1901)
SELECTED WORKS FOR PIANO

Compiled and Edited by Keith Snell

GP399

CONTENTS

D1369593

ISBN 0-8497-6269-3

GP399

THEME AND VARIATION

Theme
Allegretto

© 1999 Neil A. Kjos Music Company

Variation

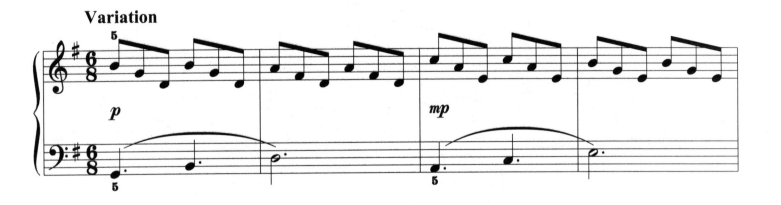

A Sad Story

THE RETURN

© 1999 Neil A. Kjos Music Company

THE STORM

Allegro non troppo

GAVOTTE

SCHERZO

DANGEROUS ADVENTURE

A Day in the Park

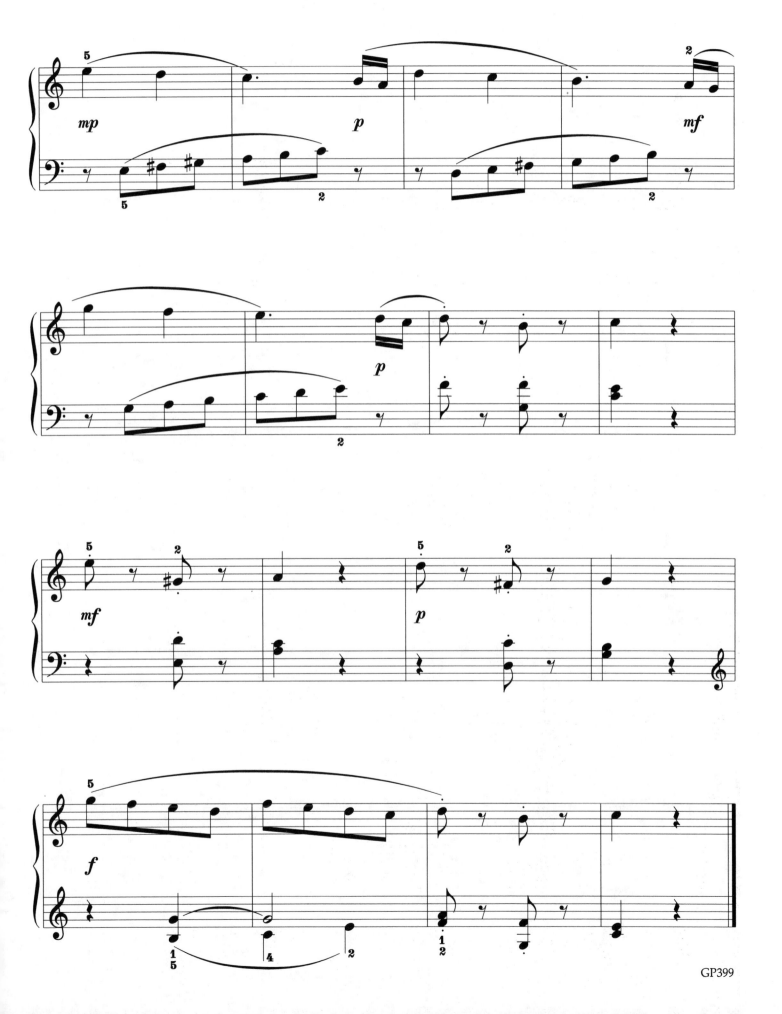

AFTERNOON FUN

DRAMATIC EVENT

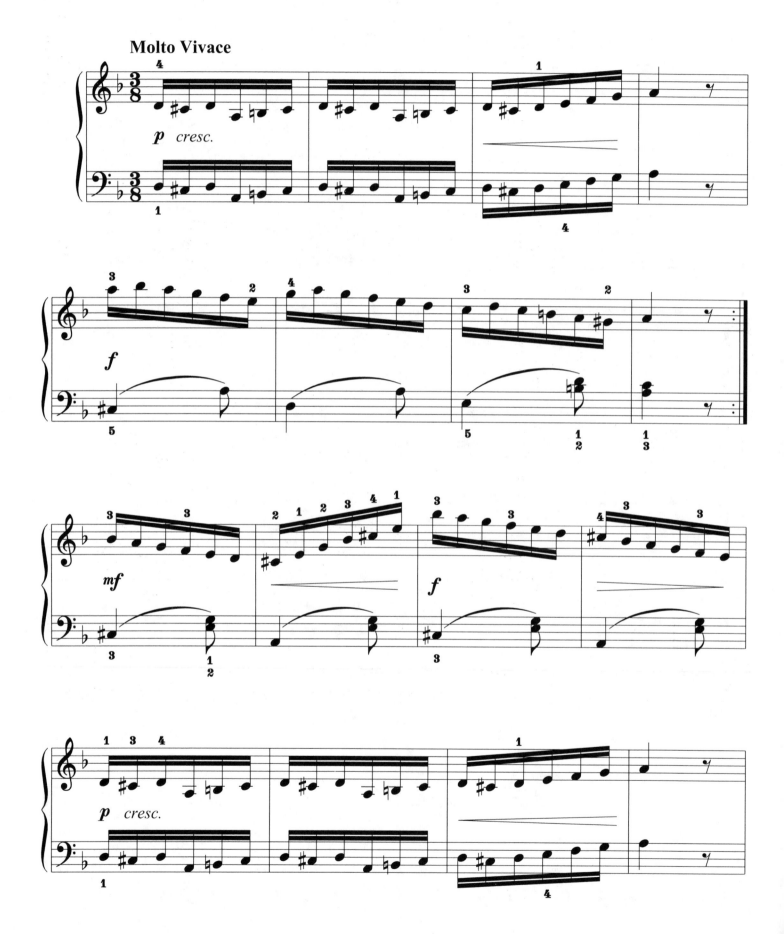

© 1999 Neil A. Kjos Music Company

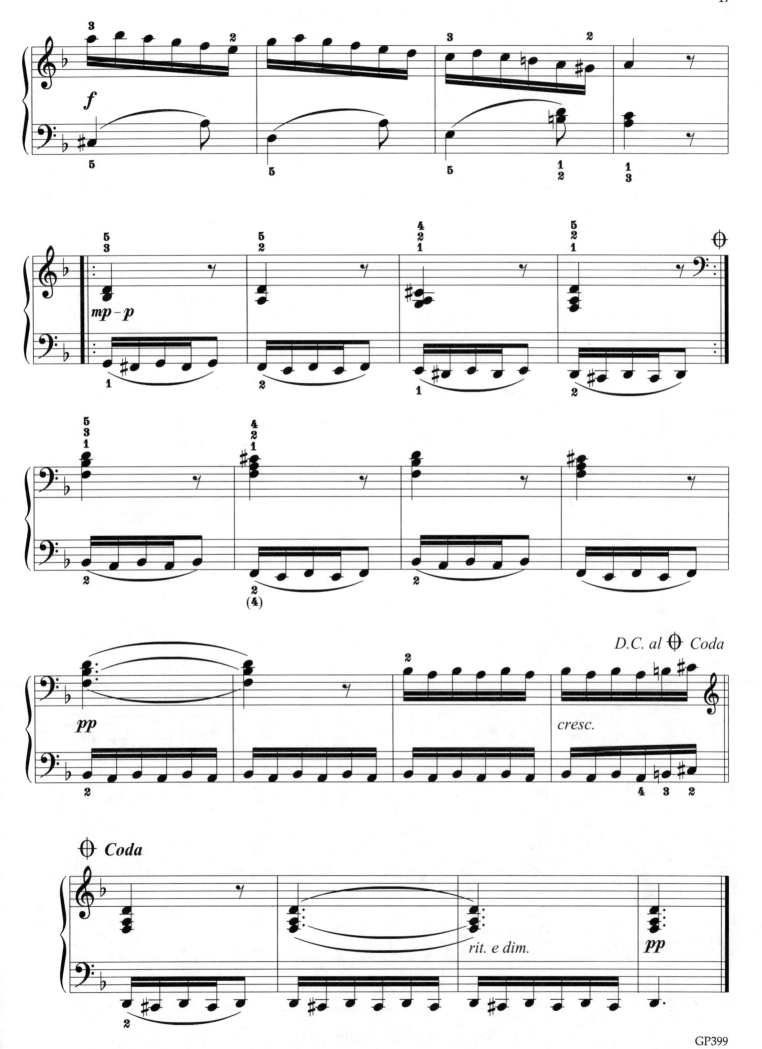

FOND MEMORY

D.C. al Fine

SONATINA

© 1999 Neil A. Kjos Music Company

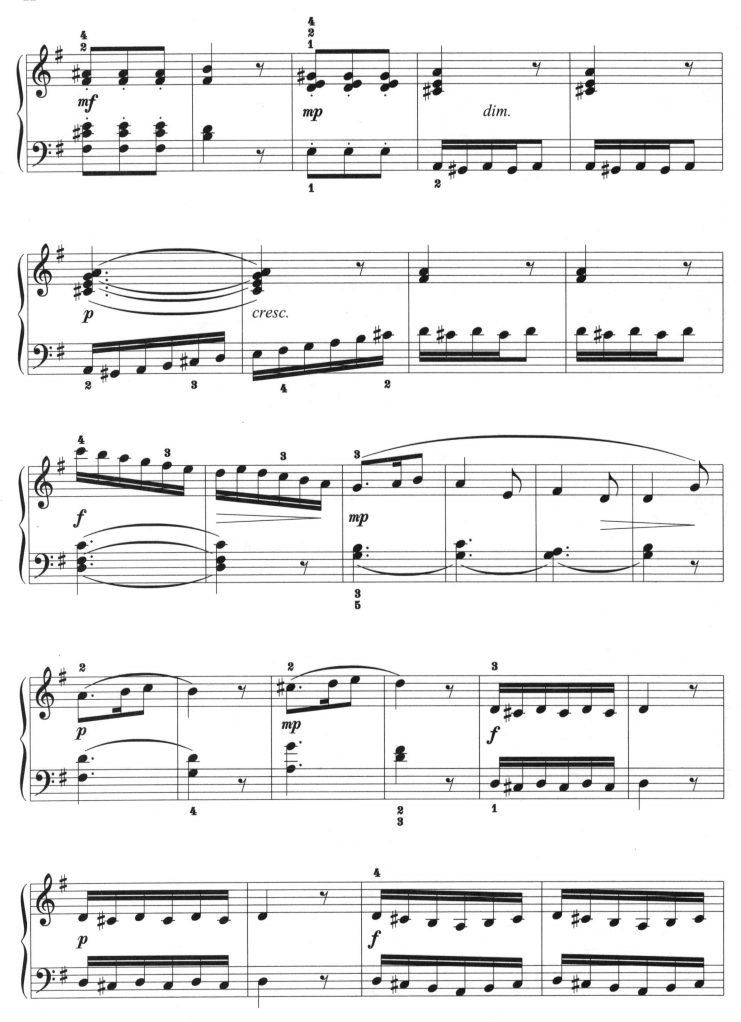

ON THE SLOPES